Praise for *The Little Boo*

CW00537432

"Heather has done a brilliant job
lemonade in her journey from ca
of her to share this step-by-step account we can all benefit from.
Thanks, Heather."

Stella Parton

International award-winning singer/songwriter and author of *Tell It Sister,
Tell It*, *Really Cookin'*, *Country Cookin'*, and *State Fairs and Church Bazaars*

"Heather does a great job in this book of helping readers under-
stand the process of cancer. Whether you recently got diagnosed
or have a loved one who has. I'd highly recommend applying the
principles from *The Little Book of Healing!*"

Brandon Gaydorus

Author of four books and founder of Warm Heart Life

"Heather is an open, caring, and thoughtful person. She is completely vulnerable as she shares her deeply personal journey through
cancer. She reveals insights into herself and her attitudes toward
God, others, recovery, and miracles that are inspiring. Her goal is to
help others struggling through cancer and any adversity. 'You are
not alone!' could be tattooed on her forehead, if it wasn't so evident
in her smile when she greets you. Thank you, Heather!"

Scott Campbell

Realtor® C2EX® PMC® SRES®, Nourmand & Associates, Los Angeles

"Brava, Heather! Your story of perseverance is truly inspiring. Your words are a precious gift to those traveling through the dark corridor of cancer looking for the light."

Cindy Frank
Dear friend, tech executive, creator, and entrepreneur;
co-founder, The Live Forward Project

"This is a MUST read for anyone who is going through cancer or has a loved one battling cancer. It is raw and real and provides the spiritual touch that is so often missed in traditional medicine. Heather is one of the sweetest and most passionate people I know and to read her words is nothing short of breathtaking. This book will provide some relief for those battling this nasty disease."

Ashley Peed
Nutrition coach, The Daily Pursuit™

"Your courage, kindness, and strength shine throughout this book. Your message of hope, giving and receiving love, encouragement, and support is powerful."

Tina Crownover
Certified Lymphedema Therapist, Licensed Massage Therapist

"Heather is a powerhouse who has been through it all and is still standing. In this book, she shares her journey through unexpected crises, grief, and uncertainty. All the while, her faith kept her going. This book is an empowering read."

Zahra Heydari LMFT
Licensed Mental Health Professional, Holistic therapist/coach, and author of *Stop the Bleeding*

"I enjoyed every line, every word, of this engaging and courageous account of the story of my patient Heather Thurman, one of the kindest and most thoughtful people I have ever met. And what a great story! It was my privilege to serve Heather during her fight with breast cancer and find that perfect option for her for her breast cancer reconstruction in such a time of pain and struggle. This heartfelt and honest description carries us as readers through her devastating diagnosis, her path to conquering not one, but two cancers, and realizing the great life and successes that God has planned for her after her cancer victory. Heather's story is one of perseverance, faith, strength, and blessings. How grateful am I to know her and celebrate her life and her success!"

Kent "Kye" Higdon, MD, FACS
Board Certified Plastic Surgeon, Aesthetic Surgery and
Breast Reconstruction Specialist, Nashvillle

"*The Little Book of Healing* is an inspiring and encouraging narrative. I wish I had known about many of these facets of treatment at the beginning of my cancer journey. Heather's story includes trusting yourself and creating a new outlook on life. We all need hope. This little missive does just that. Thank you for writing a helpful book on healing."

Mary Warren
Missionary and Co-Founder & Director, Leadership International
8 Year Survivor

"Heather Thurman became a Survivor the day she was diagnosed with breast cancer! In *The Little Book of Healing,* Heather shares the details of her personal story of being diagnosed with, dealing with, and healing from cancer. Heather told me she wanted to write this book years ago. I applaud her for being vulnerable and recounting her emotional story to help other people and their families going through cancer. Heather lives out Romans 8:28: 'And we know that God causes all things to work together for good to those who love God, to those who are called according to His purpose.' Thank you, Heather, for writing *The Little Book of Healing* and showing others the hope in the diagnosis and how to thrive through cancer."

Tracie Lathram Shelby
15 Year Survivor

"*The Little Book of Healing* is a poignant, thought-provoking and faith-affirming survival kit for anyone who is navigating a cancer diagnosis or life-threatening disease.

Well organized in a workshop format, Heather expresses raw, genuine, relatable emotions and solutions, as well as positive strategies to ease fears and anxieties. I wish I could have been equipped with this survival kit when I was diagnosed with breast cancer at the age of 46.

I am grateful now to share *The Little Book of Healing* with friends and family. A must have in my library."

Teena J. Miller
20 Year Survivor

"Heather's story is not one about living with cancer, but one about truly *living*. She beautifully shares how she fought to heal on many levels and created meaning in every step she took. An encouraging life story for anyone struggling to find their way through their own adversity."

Jennifer Thames
Licensed Marriage and Family Therapist

"Heather Thurman has written a beautiful and motivational book about her experience with cancer and her advice for people who have to experience similar journeys. Over the years, I have seen patients that hold the beauty of positivity and strength leading to improved experiences with a cancer diagnosis, and Heather shares her personal positivity as a gift for the reader."

Dana M. Chase, MD, FACOG
Associate Professor, Division of Gynecologic Oncology, Department of Obstetrics & Gynecology, David Geffen School of Medicine at UCLA

the
little
book
of
healing

the
little
book
of
healing

thriving through cancer

Heather Thurman

ISBN: 979-8-9901546-0-5 (paperback)
ISBN: 979-8-9901546-1-2 (ebook)

Book design by G Sharp Design, LLC

A portion of the proceeds of the sale of this book will go towards eradicating breast and uterine cancer.

For Liz and Sarah

INTRODUCTION

DON'T QUIT

Hello Friend,

   If you found this book, most likely you or a loved one have been diagnosed with cancer.

   You probably feel a ton of different emotions, just like I did. I wrote this book with you in mind. As I journeyed through cancer, I wrote about my experiences, hoping to someday help you. I'm here for you. Your journey will surely be different than mine because each of us has our own path and our own purpose. For me, it was a blessing to get sick. That may sound strange, but as you go through your own journey, it will make more sense.

I watched for the blessings along the way. I hope you will do that, too. I met so many awesome people through it all. Not just doctors and nurses, but people who also had some type of cancer. They inspired me and kept me going. I was also blessed to have supportive daughters and friends who were there for me.

But ultimately, I had to fight for myself. You see, I had spent most of my life caring for others. I put others before myself and really didn't know how to ask for what I needed or wanted. It was a wake-up call for me. I had barely traveled or dreamed. I had fallen asleep to what life can truly be. But cancer . . . cancer gave me the gift of life.

Choose life, and you will not be sorry. Don't quit on you. You've got this. Believe in your inner strength, and if you don't have enough of that, then grow it. You can change and grow if you feel you need to. Take a breath, take a walk, eat a good green salad, and make a plan. Take it one breath at a time if you need to. Don't be afraid to ask for help. God hears you and has a way of showing up. Now, you need to show up, too.

With love,

Heather

CHAPTER 1

YOU ARE A SURVIVOR

One day you will tell your story of how you
overcame what you went through
and it will be someone else's survival guide.

BRENÉ BROWN

Oh my gosh, that hurts, I thought as the nurse smashed my breast into a pancake. With my shoulder exposed, my body shivered in the white Vanderbilt Breast Center robe.

"Hold that handle on the right," the cheery nurse directed.

I was feeling pretty good about myself; I always made sure I scheduled a yearly mammogram. Yes, I had missed a year, but that's because I'd been so busy.

"Perfect," she said. "Now, hold your breath: one, two, three"—the machine made a roaring sound—"now breathe."

I was running through the things I needed to do that afternoon in my head. *Do we have stuff for dinner? What is Sarah doing tonight? Did I pay the water bill?*

"Okay, breathe," the nurse said again.

I need to pay more attention.

"Ms. Thurman, wait here while I make sure I got enough images."

What? Why?

It seemed like an unusually long time before she returned.

"Ms. Thurman, we need to get some additional images. It looks like there's some calcification in the right breast, so we need to go ahead and do an ultrasound while you are here. The head of imaging just happens to be here today. She will take care of you."

They whisked me to another room. It was dimly lit and had calming pictures on the walls.

Breathe, I thought.

An hour went by. The air felt heavy. Was it just my imagination?

I'm just really tired; it's Friday, for heaven's sake.

The doctor returned, and I will never forget the look in her eyes. I knew words were coming from her mouth, but all I could see were her eyes. Her look shot right through my soul.

"Ms. Thurman, there is an unusual calcification in the right breast. We did not see that the last time you were imaged. It is of unknown significance, but I am going to schedule a stereotactic biopsy to determine what we are looking at."

Could this be cancer? I thought. But I said nothing.

I went home. I resolved to not jump to any conclusions, and so I didn't. Honestly, I couldn't even go there.

It All Begins—The Biopsies

My appointments at Vanderbilt moved quickly and yet way too slowly. Finally, a week and a half later, I drove myself to my scheduled stereotactically guided breast biopsy at One Hundred Oaks.

It was a beautiful day in August; the flowers were in full bloom and the air smelled like magnolias. On my way in, I ran into an old friend who had brought his elderly mother for a doctor's appointment. I casually told him what I was there for, and he looked surprised that I was alone. It was Sarah's first week back to school; it didn't even occur to me to get someone to drive me.

Lying face down with my chest through a hole in the table, I tried to think relaxing thoughts.

Three nurses and the same doctor from my last appointment scurried around. They numbed my chest and the procedure began: forty-five minutes of slowly removing tissue through a large needle moving in and out of my breast. The sound of the drilling was disturbing.

Thoughts started swirling around in my head. *Why am I here alone? Who do I really have to help me through this?*

Sadness crept in. For the first time in a long time, I was forced to slow down and think. I thought about how I didn't feel fulfilled as a person. I just lay there and thought.

After the procedure, they wrapped my chest in a huge bandage that was supposed to stop the bleeding.

For the first time in a long time, I was forced to slow down and think.

I looked like a partial mummy. The bandage was so tight I could barely breathe, and I was famished.

I somehow mustered the strength to drive home and get myself into bed. The bandage became soaked with my blood, and I was alarmed; I had never been very good with the sight of blood. Over the next several hours, I made two calls to the doctors on call, and finally, at about two in the morning the bleeding stopped.

The stereotactic biopsy showed that I had atypical cells, and the doctor recommended a surgical biopsy. She told me that in 10 percent of cases, these atypical cells can be invasive breast cancer, but most likely it was nothing. After hearing that, I almost decided to not have the surgical biopsy. I really didn't think I could possibly have anything but healthy cells. But I went ahead with it.

During the first biopsy, they had inserted a metal "marker" in the place where they thought the cancer was located. Based on that marker, the second biopsy would remove a greater portion of cells in order to test them.

It was seven weeks before my surgical biopsy was performed. Seven weeks of meeting with surgeons, which included a heart echo test after I felt dizzy and faintish one day while shopping at Target. I had called one of the nurses to tell them how I felt, and they recommended I have a heart test to make sure I was healthy enough for surgery. I did, and I was.

Seven weeks of sales calls and dinners and homework and trying to maintain my sanity. Seven weeks of semi-denial. Seven weeks of trying to distract myself.

When the day of the surgery came in late September, it seemed almost trivial. Sarah's high school had all their homecoming festivities that day, and I was fine with her skipping the surgery and living her life. Liz, my older daughter, was kind enough to drive me, and the plan was for me to go home right after I got out of recovery.

The surgery was over before I knew it, and rather than being exhausted, I felt great. It was like I had had a reboot of some kind; I had never felt so energized. I wondered if the anesthesia had given me the rest I never had but desperately needed.

A Devastating Diagnosis

Two weeks later, on October 9, I asked Sarah if she wanted to go to my post-op appointment with me. I asked her last minute because I had planned to go alone. She was in school, and Liz was working; it was going to be routine, and I didn't want to waste anyone's time.

She agreed to go with me, so I signed Sarah out of school, and we drove to the Breast Center at One Hundred Oaks. It was a busy place that day; the waiting room was packed with women, some with their husband or a friend.

They called my name, handed me a hospital gown that looked more like a robe, and guided me to the small room that included a patient chair, a table, and a small desk. A curtain divided this part of the room from two other chairs. Pamphlets about breast cancer were in little bins on the back of the door. A blood pressure machine hung on the wall.

My incision was healing nicely, and I was looking forward to seeing Dr. Kelley, the surgical oncologist. After I got changed into my gown, I sat on the end of the patient examination table and waited. I felt sure I would be okay. I was calm.

There was a faint knock at the door, and in came Dr. Kelley and my favorite nurse.

Dr. Kelley started speaking immediately.

"The cells we thought were atypical cells—well, we found invasive breast cancer as well as cancer in your milk ducts. It was a 90 percent chance it was nothing, but you are in the 10 percent."

My head started to swim. "What did you say, Dr. Kelley?"

"You have breast cancer."

My mind couldn't accept what my ears were hearing. I just sat there. I felt faint.

"Do you need to lie down?" He put his hand on my back and helped me recline.

No. I can't have cancer. How do I have cancer?

My mind raced with thoughts about raising Sarah, my job, and what would happen to me. What *was* happening to me? I felt overcome.

I composed myself and sat up.

"Do you have any questions?" Dr. Kelley asked.

"Questions? I don't even know what to ask you. I know next to nothing about breast cancer."

I felt like a bomb had just detonated my hearing. All I could hear was the word *cancer*.

On our way back to the car, Sarah and I went into a store next to the breast center called Pretty in Pink.

It was a store for breast cancer patients. I slumped into the chair by the cashier.

"They just told me I have breast cancer . . . but I don't feel sick," I heard myself say to the manager.

"That's what everyone says," she told me.

After the appointment, I was in shock. Of course, my first thought as a single mom was, "How is this going to impact my livelihood?" I had no idea what this diagnosis really meant. The only thing I knew was that I somehow had to tell my boss, Lance.

Sarah and I drove directly to my office from One Hundred Oaks, and I walked straight into Lance's office at Health Stream.

"You're not going to believe this," I said.

The hospital had given me a neatly put together binder of my surgical results and information on breast cancer. On the cover it said, *My Handbook: Tools for Learning.* Inside it had a tab and label for *Diagnosis and Treatment, Logs/Notes, Education,* and *Glossary.*

I just set the binder on his desk.

He must have been floored; he had this look on his face like he didn't really know what to say or do. I've since learned that when you're in shock, you don't remember a lot of the details. I don't remember exactly what Lance said that day. But I do remember that he was positive and understanding. Somehow he found words that encouraged me and put me at ease.

I had an MRI to determine whether there was cancer in the left breast, too, and what the best surgical options would be. My mother, bless her heart, took several trips to Whole Foods to buy healthy greens and nourishing food for me to eat.

I called my nurse navigator one afternoon on the drive home and talked with her. She told me it was normal for close family members to get really upset.

"Don't take it personally," she said.

Wait a minute—am I not the one with cancer?

Nevertheless, I tried to follow her advice.

Tracie, a breast cancer survivor in my neighborhood, called me soon after I was diagnosed. She had a positive, bubbly personality, and we spoke for quite a while. I had so many questions, and she did her best to answer them all. Tracie told me that I was a survivor from the moment I was diagnosed. That concept seemed a bit foreign, but it was one I tried to accept. She told me about the Susan G. Komen race and the survivor tent, and how every year she went and looked forward to getting the pink breast cancer emblem to put on her hat to mark another year of being cancer-free.

One day, she stopped by to bring me a care package with a pink heart-shaped bean-filled pillow to heat in the microwave, a pink hat from the race, and a colorful scarf. Her friendship and encouragement meant a lot.

During this time, I found solace in nature. I spent time alone outside whenever I could. Even as the days grew colder, I would still bundle up and at least sit in the sun. I noticed that the bees had gone into hibernation, and the birds were chirping less. I enjoyed the stillness.

At the same time, work was getting harder. Before cancer, I had been crushing it. Now I struggled to make my calls and even get the words out.

I was losing my desire to do this job, which made me feel incredibly guilty. I didn't want to let my boss down, my daughters down, my sales team down. What was I to do?

As the flood of emotions kept coming, I began journaling. I realized that I was carrying around so much guilt—not just about my job, but about my failed marriage, about all this attention, even for being so strong at times. Most of all, I felt guilt for all the people I'd be letting down now that I was sick: my mom, my daughters, my friends, my co-workers. . . I wasn't able to be me anymore. I was a broken version of myself. At least, that's how I felt.

Tracie had invited me to walk in the annual Susan G. Komen Race for the Cure, but I wasn't ready. When I was leaving work one day, they were setting up for the race right outside our parking lot and were blocking the road. I had to turn around, and I got really angry.

Really? Haven't I been inconvenienced enough?

I was also feeling sorry for myself.

It's not fair. Hasn't my life been tough enough? Where are you in all this, God?

More than anything, the not knowing felt unbearable. Not knowing if I would lose my hair. Not knowing if I'd lose my breasts. Not knowing if I would make it through this.

I began to remember some past difficult events in my life. Even though life had been hard at times, I had always retained a spark that hadn't been affected. Part of me had still been so carefree and innocent. Now I had lost that, too. It felt like my spark was gone.

I grieved the loss of my before-cancer life. I grieved being a whole family. I grieved being the person who broke sales records, who sometimes set the bar for others. That woman was gone.

The Decision to Fight for My Life

But something else happened early on, too.

One dreary afternoon, I sat in my office, again struggling to make the phone calls I needed to make to meet my sales goals. My hands were shaking as I dialed the numbers.

At the same time, I also had this tender, bloated, uncomfortable feeling in my abdomen. I called my gynecologist, who scheduled an ultrasound of my uterus.

I had so many decisions to make at every turn.

That's when it hit me: I had spent my whole life fighting for others. But if I didn't make it, I wouldn't be able to fight for them. Who was going to fight for *me*?

That day, November 11, I chose to fight for myself.

I decided to not let cancer win. I decided to live.

"Cancer be gone!" I proclaimed over myself. I read and reread two verses:

I had spent my whole life fighting for others. But who was going to fight for me?

"I tell you the truth, you can say to this mountain, 'May you be lifted up and thrown into the sea,' and it will happen. But you must really believe it will happen and have no doubt in your heart." (Mark 11:23)

"I will not die, but live, and tell of the works of the Lord." (Psalm 118:17)

I refocused my drive at work and mustered every bit of courage I had.

I was going to fight cancer.

No matter what it took from me or did to me, I was going to fight it.

With everything I had.

I wish I could give you a big hug right now. If you have been diagnosed with cancer, it's essential that you tap into your inner strength and faith. I believe there is a Higher Power that works for our good. Healing can occur over time, but it can also be miraculous. I know people who have healed from stage 4 cancers. We each have our journey and way of facing this. There is no right or wrong way—there is only your way.

Decide to be a survivor. You are already advocating for yourself by choosing to read this little book. When I received my diagnosis, one of the first things I did was to make a vision board of the life I intended to live. It might be a good thing for you to do now. Make a vision board of things you want to do in your life after you survive. Places you want to see, that special house, etc. Get your passport. Believe. Believe with every cell of your being that you will get through this. Start journaling because you won't remember details later. Read inspirational books that feed your soul. Get out in nature as much as you can. Pray daily.

I also had to work on worthiness. That might not apply to you, but I felt guilty for being sick. I didn't feel like I deserved the attention, and it made me realize that I didn't love myself deeply. I didn't really accept myself. I've done a lot of meditations on this topic, as well as courses and therapy. (Thank you to my counselors, Jennifer and Zahra!) I needed to dig deep into why I felt unworthy of love. That unworthiness affected all areas of my life:

relationships, work, etc. I have since healed this part of me, and it has empowered me.

How will you fight for yourself today?

_____

_____

_____

_____

CHAPTER 2

FIND YOUR SUPPORT SYSTEM

Alone we can do so little; together
we can do so much.

HELEN KELLER

E ven after my decision to fight for myself, I felt very alone. I had sunk into a depression. It felt like a deep well. Even though I knew I wasn't alone, it felt like I was.

I needed people to press in. To show up.

Sarah's lacrosse team really surprised me! I wasn't able to cook, and Sarah was in high school.

The coach created a calendar where families could sign up to bring us meals. They brought meals faithfully after every surgery for weeks. Most of these families were strangers, but they cared enough to make us delicious food. They even called to ask what we liked. Those meals nourished us body and soul. They made a huge difference in my healing.

Another very touching thing was that my boyfriend's children made me a prayer journal and brought me flowers and candy for Valentine's Day. Those gifts made me feel very loved and contributed to my healing.

People I barely knew were filling in the gaps in our lives. For example, a co-worker came to talk with me when he found out that his girlfriend, who was in her early thirties, had been diagnosed with stage four colon cancer, and we supported each other. Also, while new furniture was being installed at our office, I ended up talking with one of the workers whose wife had gone through cancer. The next day he brought me a pin and a little bracelet his wife had made.

Those small acts of kindness from strangers may seem insignificant, but for me they were very meaning-

Those small acts of
kindness from strangers
may seem insignificant,
but for me they were "God
winks"—reminders that
I am not forgotten.

ful and what I call "God winks"—reminders that I am not forgotten.

Soon after I was diagnosed, I attended a Gilda's Club meeting for people with cancer. (It's also called Cancer Support Community in some cities). We all sat in a semicircle and took turns introducing ourselves. Each one of us had been diagnosed with a different kind of cancer, except one girl whose dad had died from cancer.

As I listened intently to each story, I was amazed to realize that I felt really strong. When it was my turn, I thought it would be easy to give the elevator version of my story, like everyone else had.

The moment I opened my mouth, though, it was like a dam broke, and I started sobbing. I couldn't say a word, but after a few moments, I was able to get something out. I think it was because it was the very first time I admitted to myself that I had cancer. This was real.

Afterward, we all went downstairs, and by the door was a bin of little knit hats for people going through chemo. Maybe I would need chemo, too. I didn't know. I took one on my way out.

Spiritual Support and Journaling

Before too long, I was desperate for some spiritual support, so I reached out to a lady at church named Suzanne. She was a single mother who always seemed at peace, no matter what was going on in her life. We had spoken a couple times over the past few years and had volunteered together in the inner city, but I really didn't know her that well. I knew she did some counseling, though.

She and her close friend Brenda counseled together as a team, and they offered to counsel me. Once a week, I would drive to Suzanne's house, and she and Brenda started walking with me through my cancer journey.

Over time, Suzanne became what I would call my spiritual counselor. She suggested I read a book called *The Silver Lining*, written by her mother-in-law who was a stage four colon cancer survivor. So, I did. She urged me to take Communion daily and speak life over myself. So, I did. She suggested that I write. So, I did. Twenty days after I was diagnosed, I began to journal. I wrote all the details of my own story so I could remember them later. I wrote through all the emotional ups and downs so characteristic of a cancer journey.

Writing was truly a lifeline for me. It helped me in so many ways:

- ✾ It helped me feel grounded.
- ✾ It gave me a feeling of purpose.
- ✾ It made me feel less alone.
- ✾ It filled me with a hope that transcended the pain.

In its own way, cancer gave me a respite from my hectic life. It gave me the time off I desperately needed. Looking back, it was a wake-up call to discover myself, to slow down and evaluate how I was living my life. In my journal, I asked myself:

How had I gotten here?
Where was I going?
How did I feel?

Suddenly, what I liked and didn't like about my life became incredibly clear. Some parts of my life I loved, but others felt like duty. For instance, I realized I loved sales, but I didn't like being inside all day. I loved my co-workers, but I didn't feel like my life as a whole was firing on all cylinders. At the same time, as a single parent, I had certain responsibilities whether I liked

Looking back, cancer
was a wake-up call to
discover myself, to slow
down and evaluate how
I was living my life.

them or not. As my mother, another single mom, constantly told me as a child: "It ain't what you like." I interpreted this to mean that you accept life for what it throws at you. You accept less. By the way, I have learned that is a **limiting belief**, and it **is** what you like.

I felt raw. I felt out of control. I felt helpless. I wrote through all of it.

God Appointments

But I also felt hopeful, because I seemed to be meeting breast cancer survivors at every turn—women with knowledge who wanted to come alongside me and encourage me.

My friend Tracie was there for me.

Allie, another survivor, and her husband Nate stopped by to give me *Dr. Susan Love's Breast Book*—a tome of helpful information—and two kinds of my favorite chocolate cake from a local restaurant. They offered to pray with me. This meant a lot.

Michael and Sissy, an older couple from my church, also came to my home to pray with me. Sissy had had a miraculous healing when she and Michael were first married, and she gave me a bracelet with the word *Miracles*. I felt as though life was being poured into me with every visit and every prayer.

I also seemed to randomly meet supportive people who were people of prayer. For example, not long after I was diagnosed, my mom, Sarah, and I were at the Whole Foods salad bar when my mom began telling a woman that I was going through cancer. That woman happened to be a pastor at New Song Christian Fellowship, the first church we had attended when we moved to Tennessee from Northern California. Right in the middle of Whole Foods, the pastor asked if she could pray with me, and it meant so much.

At Target, I ran into Susie, a friend I hadn't seen in years. She and I had been co-leaders in Bible Study Fellowship. We had really bonded during that time, and as a gift she had even redecorated my home. I told Susie what had happened, and she said she'd pray for me.

At the gas station, I saw Brian, one of my previous pastors from Grace Center. He also prayed with me and said he would continue to pray.

I began to call these random encounters "God appointments." Those meetings gave me courage. I believed they were signs that God was watching over me.

With each act of love and compassion, I felt like I wasn't forgotten. As a single, divorced mom, I often felt forgotten. Yes, some of my friends did disappear. But I also learned that people deal with trauma in different ways. Some come closer as a result; some run from it. The only thing I could do was accept people where they were. That was another lesson for me.

Even so, I remember fighting depression. I had always been a positive person, a go-getter. Never in my life had I felt so down and so discouraged. During a specific part of this journey, during the day I felt supported, but at night a dark cloud would come over me. I lost some of my sense of humor. Even though I knew people were praying for me and rooting for me I struggled with feeling down.

Here, too, support came at just the right time. Cindy, one of my very closest friends, invited me out for coffee at Frothy Monkey, one of my favorite places to this day. I've known Cindy for twenty-plus years, and she's amazing—just a real badass kind of a woman.

I began to call these random encounters "God appointments." Those meetings gave me courage.

She's intelligent, beautiful, successful, and athletic. She'd also been through a divorce and has been a single mom for many years. Now her children are grown.

Cindy is one of the strongest women I know. I just sat across from her at Frothy, thinking, *I miss feeling strong. I miss* being *strong. I miss having drive and determination.*

As if she could hear my thoughts, Cindy began to pour strength into me. She reminded me of all my strengths. She encouraged me to find something to look forward to and to write a list of all the things I love to do. I had been raised to pull myself up by my bootstraps, which hadn't been working very well for me. She pulled me out of that deep, dark place by helping me remember who I was and reminding me that I still have dreams unfulfilled—and I could decide to keep going for them.

I don't know exactly how, but I remember just snapping out of that horrible darkness when I was with Cindy that day. If a close friend can really be there for you and remind you of who you are, it can mean everything.

Cindy's support helped me to support others. For example, I found myself reaching out to the people I met in the doctor's waiting room who were facing cancer or another struggle. I would always ask them about their story. There wasn't much time to go deep, but it felt good to let them know they weren't alone.

The first time I went to the Ingram Cancer Center in downtown Nashville, it reminded me of the DMV: the hustle and bustle was overwhelming. After I got checked in, I went across the hall to a huge room where it was much calmer. Someone was playing the piano, and in the corner was a large plant with encouraging handwritten messages hanging from it on tiny cards. Those messages were heartwarming and hopeful.

As I waited to be called, I struck up a conversation with the young lady sitting next to me. Her name was Racheta, and she had lymphoma. I listened to her as she described her family and her challenges—her mom had to move in with her; her kids were loud; and she couldn't rest. As a young, single mother, she had difficulty getting to treatments because she had to take the bus.

My heart hurt for her. "I'm going to be praying for you," I said.

That was the first of many cancer patients I met along the way. From that moment on, I made a point of looking around me, talking to people, asking them about their stories, and writing their names down so I could pray for them.

I met so many interesting people. I started a list on my iPhone, and I ended up with a long list of names along with the kind of cancer or challenge they were facing. I would pray for them as well as for myself. I realized I was not alone in this fight. There were others fighting, too, and I could support them. It gave me joy to pray for them. I often wonder how they are doing today.

Everyone has their own way of going through things, but I highly recommend putting together your support "team." Who can you call to pray for you, go to appointments with you, encourage you? Don't be afraid to ask for what you need. Some of us aren't great at asking for help. Keep an eye out for the "God winks" in your own journey—those unexpected reminders that let you know you're not alone or forgotten.

Weed out those toxic people in your life who are negative. You know who I'm talking about. Remove them from your life or at least limit contact with them. You need every bit of physical and emotional strength to go through this journey. Life goes on, even with cancer. It's kind of a weird feeling.

I've mentioned Gilda's Club, also known as Cancer Support Community. Being part of a support community helps you feel less alone. Even though your friends and family are supportive, they don't truly know what you are going through. Only those who have gone through it know. I was also part of Susan G. Komen and the YMCA ABC (After Breast Cancer) group. Each played a part in my healing.

On a practical note, find a nurse navigator, if your medical practice has one. My nurse navigator was extremely helpful; she helped coordinate appointments as well as being there for us emotionally. She was a huge blessing.

Who is on your support team? What is one way you can ask for help today?

_____

_____

_____

_____

CHAPTER 3

MAKE A PLAN

It's not the plan that's important, it's the planning.

DR. GRAEME EDWARDS

Time slowed down. Every hour felt like a day; every day felt like a week. All I could do was decide what I was going to do right now, in that moment.

After I was diagnosed, I called my friend Teena. She is a breast cancer survivor and had recently moved to Colorado. She told me to buy greens and take a walk every day. I found her simple instructions reassuring; she understood the heaviness I felt and tried to give me something practical to do.

One of the first things my neighbor Tracie said to me was "IGBOK."

"What?" I asked.

"It's an acronym. It means It's Going to Be OK. Now, what's your plan?"

She was really open about different kinds of treatments and the feelings I would experience, and she helped me formulate my plan, which at that point was to get a lumpectomy and radiation. She also loaned me some nighties designed for after surgeries. They were beautiful and very helpful.

Tracie also gave talks about breast cancer at Vanderbilt University. She kept emphasizing that having a plan gives focus and a course of action. If things changed, as they often would, I would create a new plan. And it was going to be OK.

I kept going back to my plan for the day, for the week, for my treatment. Having a plan saved me. It gave me some sense of control.

I had to balance work, caring for my mom, parenting, and scheduling the upcoming lumpectomy and doctor appointments. Simple, but also complicated at the same time.

Next Steps

The table was cold on my behind; the robe was stiff from bleach. I was waiting in the examination room for my surgical oncologist, Dr. Kelley, to talk about next steps after my biopsy.

On my own, I had decided that instead of having a lumpectomy and radiation, I wanted a bilateral mastectomy—both breasts removed. I had a lot of cancer in my ducts, so to me that meant there was a risk of not getting it all with a lumpectomy.

Also, with a mastectomy, I most likely wouldn't need radiation. I had thought through the amount of time it would take to drive back and forth to radiation treatments, how hard radiation can be on the body, and how much work I might have to miss. A bilateral mastectomy meant less down time and less time away from work.

It might sound extreme, but the way I saw it, a lumpectomy was already a partial mastectomy. Plus, one of my friends had one breast removed and later had to have the other removed—and she said she had wished she had done both from the beginning. With both removed, I could be reconstructed to match, and after all, this was about my survival and being here for the people who needed me.

A bilateral mastectomy just seemed more efficient all around. I felt clear about my decision.

I heard voices murmuring outside the door.

Dr. Kelley walked in unceremoniously with three other doctors.

I took a deep breath and did my best to explain my decision.

"No, that's *too* radical," said Dr. Kelley, in his typical low-key, matter-of-fact demeanor.

I hesitated. "Well, Dr. Kelley, it's less time off work, and you'll know you've gotten all the cancer."

"We can get the cancer with a lumpectomy. You don't need to take that route."

I'm not one of those people who over-researches and over-trusts the internet, but for some reason, my intuition kept telling me I should get a bilateral mastectomy. However, Dr. Kelley was one of the top guys at Vanderbilt, and I really wanted to trust him.

"Are you sure?" I asked.

"Yes, I am sure."

So, lumpectomy it was. We scheduled the surgery for a few days before Thanksgiving.

My nurse navigator, who had already been so helpful, suggested I participate in the Hope Connection. This group assigns you to a breast cancer mentor who has had a similar kind of cancer and a similar kind of procedure.

Even though I was getting a lumpectomy, they partnered me with a woman who'd had a mastectomy on one side and was doing well. Her name was Karen, and she owned a fitness studio in East Nashville. She was there to listen, to answer any questions I might have, and just be supportive. It felt really comforting to know she had been through something similar, and she shared a lot of good insights with me.

She talked me off the ledge a few times, when I was overwhelmed by all the uncertainty of breast cancer. There's so much you just don't know during treatment, and for someone like me who likes to be in control, it was really difficult. I felt like I was in free fall most of the time.

During one of my breast center appointments, a nurse told me that some women diagnosed with cancer decide not to seek treatment. I get it—the onslaught of medical information, choices, and appointments can be overwhelming. If I've learned anything from this process, though, it's that you really have to be your own advocate. I can't imagine how someone would do it if they weren't a self-starter. My nurse navigator was a big help.

The Big Day

Finally, the day of the surgery came. First, a surgical mammography machine inserted a long, hooked wire deep into my breast, which would guide the surgeon to the area where the cancer was. I guess this procedure was supposed to be minor, because I was sitting up, but it was by far the worst part. Even though they had numbed me, the pain was still so severe that I almost passed out. It was like my body couldn't feel the pain, but my brain could. They had to lean me back and put cold compresses on my forehead.

Finally, they wheeled me, covered in warm blankets, to the OR.

This was it: the first step of my fight to get rid of this horrible disease. The OR was different than I had imagined; I was more alert than I expected to be, and weirdly, I was trying to set the nurses and anesthesiologists at ease. I glanced up and saw a clock on the wall. Then the anesthesiologist placed a mask on my nose and mouth.

"Okay, breathe nice and deep. I want you to count to ten for me."

"One, two . . ."

That's literally all I remember about the surgery.

I woke up in the recovery room. Sarah and Liz came in soon after, and they drove me home. I was initially surprised how quickly the hospital sent me home after a surgery, but I soon learned the routines. We stopped at the Cheesecake Factory restaurant on the way home from surgery. My daughters had ordered ahead of time, and we picked up our food and took it home. This became our new ritual. I looked forward to this delicious food; it helped us all to build small, positive things to look forward to during this time.

It was two days before Thanksgiving. Sarah had already planned a trip to go see her dad in the Florida

Keys, and I insisted she go ahead with it. Liz would be in town; she had moved in with my mom to help her out.

Friends stopped by during the day, and even though I was alone at night, I felt pretty strong, given what I had been through.

On Thanksgiving Day, my mom wasn't feeling well, so I insisted that Liz have Thanksgiving dinner at her house. I knew none of us felt like cooking, so I ordered from Cracker Barrel. The plan was for Liz to pick up the food, drop some off for me, and then go back to Mom's house. My neighbor Sissy had invited me to her house for Thanksgiving, but honestly, I just felt like being at home.

My dear friend Cindy stopped by with my favorite Starbucks drink. It was great to spend some time with her. She always made me laugh.

Then Liz arrived with food from Cracker Barrel. I didn't want Mom's food to get cold, so I told her, "You go on and take your food to Grandma's."

I set a beautiful table for myself, with a candle, a cloth napkin, and flowers. I poured a glass of red wine and ate Thanksgiving dinner alone. I wasn't sad or lonely; instead, I felt at peace and hopeful.

I left the house for the first time a week later, when Liz took me to a Christmas concert featuring one of our friends. I was determined to get dressed up for the event. I must have tried on four different dresses, trying to see what fit me. What looked best over the surgical bra? What made me feel the most feminine?

We sat in the second row, and our friend sang beautifully. He did several carols and classic songs that I love. I sang at the top of my lungs. I was so happy to be alive and on the mend.

Always Follow Your Intuition

Finally, it was time to see Dr. Kelley for the post-op appointment. In his characteristically matter-of-fact way, he said, "Well, we didn't get clear margins."

Huh?

"What does that mean?" I asked.

He explained all the details to me, which I promptly forgot. The bottom line was that they weren't convinced they got all the cancer, and they were going to have to do a mastectomy after all.

At that moment, I told myself I was never again going to back down from my intuition regarding my health. I had essentially gone through surgery for nothing. I was disappointed and a bit frustrated by the news. It felt like such a roller coaster. What next?

As Liz and I left the Vanderbilt Breast Center at One Hundred Oaks, about two blocks away I saw a BMW dealership.

I have always loved high-performance cars. My dad was a professional test driver for Ford, and he tested the Mustang on the Ford test track in Dearborn, Michigan. For a number of years, he also drove in commercials and movies. My dad taught me how to drive, and—I don't mean to brag, but—I'm a very skilled driver. It's just one of the things I know about myself.

I enjoy driving, too. It relaxes me almost all of the time. My favorite car has always been the BMW. Not to say I don't like other cars—I really like Maseratis, too—but I just love the way BMWs look. I've had pictures of them in my office, on vision boards, all sorts of places. BMWs are the quintessential high-performance car: They're not only beautiful, they also handle great. Or so I've heard. I had never actually driven one.

At that moment, I told myself
I was never again going to
back down from my intuition
regarding my health.

No time like the present, I thought.

I turned to my daughter. "Lizzy, I've always wanted to drive a BMW."

We drove to the dealership, walked in the showroom, and explained my situation to the first people we saw inside.

"I just had an appointment at Hundred Oaks, and I found out they didn't get all my breast cancer. I've always wanted to drive a BMW. Could I test-drive one? I might not have another chance later."

They grabbed one of the salesmen, and we picked out a little 300-series four-door sedan. When I opened the door, it smelled amazing, and the details—the dashboard, the leather seats—were just gorgeous.

And driving it—wow! To me, a great car feels like an extension of yourself—both highly responsive and solid. The BMW drove just like I imagined it would. When I stepped on the gas pedal, it instantly took off, yet it hugged the road. I drove on the freeway, took a spin around town, and then came back.

What a wonderful, wonderful machine. I still have a picture of me sitting in it.

A New Plan

Now I had a new plan. The mastectomy was scheduled for December 30. I quickly learned that this would be a complicated process. Basically, two surgeries had to happen at once: first removing the breasts, and then inserting the tissue expanders.

If you've never had to think about reconstruction surgery before, you probably don't want to hear this, but tissue expanders are like hollow implants with a port that the plastic surgeon inserts during mastectomy surgery after all the breast tissue is removed. Over the next six months or so, he will slowly inflate those tissue expanders until they are the size you want, whether it's a B or D or whatever. They basically blow your breasts up like a little balloon over time, allowing your skin to stretch and be ready for the implants. Then, when the plastic surgeon does the reconstruction surgery (which in my case would be six months after the mastectomy), he removes the tissue expanders, puts in the implants, and migrates fat from different parts of your body to fill in around the implant to make the breasts.

All this meant that the plastic surgeon's schedule had to be coordinated with my oncology surgeon's schedule.

At the same time, I was having another big issue. I had gotten an ultrasound of my uterus, and as a result, my gynecologist, Dr. Rush, was concerned that I might have uterine cancer, too. Apparently, the lining of the uterus was thicker than it should have been, and I also had three really large fibroids.

Clearly I had to get to the bottom of the uterine thing. Dr. Rush had already done a D&C during my lumpectomy to get uterine cells to analyze, but he didn't feel he got enough. He wanted to do another D&C during my double mastectomy, so now we had to coordinate three busy doctors' schedules.

Of course, Christmas was coming, which made it even harder. Suffice to say, the scheduler messed up, and once again I had to be my own advocate to make sure I kept the December 30th surgery date. It was important for me to have the surgery over Christmas so I didn't have to miss more work than necessary. I had to get kind of pushy, but I got all three scheduled— honestly, it was kind of a miracle.

Between the lumpectomy and the mastectomy, I was still working, trying to keep everything afloat, and preparing to be out of the office yet again.

Surgery Day

On December 30, I had my double mastectomy. After all that planning, the surgery itself was a little anticlimactic. You'd think I would have been really emotional—after all, I was going to wake up without my breasts—but oddly enough, I felt good about it. I just wanted to get it done, get rid of the cancer, and get on with life.

It was now the third time I was going under anesthesia, so I was used to the process. I got in my warming gown, which was hooked up to a vacuum-looking thing that blew out warm air under the gown. They put the elastic cap on over my hair, pulled on my special socks to keep my feet warm, hooked me up to an IV, and wheeled me into the OR.

By that time, I had a bit of a routine: I would cheerfully say as they rolled me in the OR, "Hi, everyone—how are you?" I saw Dr. Rush, so I assumed that meant they would do the D&C first, and then the mastectomy and tissue expanders. They put the anesthesia in the IV, did their countdown, and I was out.

When I woke up in the recovery room, Sarah was there.

As crazy as it sounds, they only keep you overnight for observation after this kind of surgery. From the recovery room, I was moved to a tiny room. Unfortunately, that room had a mirror in it; when I first saw myself, I was shocked. My face was greenish-yellow, and I looked like absolute hell. I had done it, though. I had gotten rid of all the cancer. My lymph nodes were negative. That was a relief, and it meant the cancer had not spread outside the breast. I would now truly be on the mend. Woo-hoo!

The Recovery Begins

On New Year's Eve, they sent me home with a pile of medicines and painkillers. By now the girls and I also had a new after-surgery routine: Together, they would pick me up from the hospital, and we would order takeout from the Cheesecake Factory in Green Hills. Yay!

Now the real recovery began. I had drains in me, which meant I couldn't shower for about six weeks, or until the drains came out. The drains themselves had to be cleaned regularly, which was a huge ordeal. This involved having someone strip out the clots and then measure the fluid that came out of them several times a day, every day. Once the fluid went down to a certain amount, the drains could be taken out. Apparently, the more active you are, the longer they have to stay in, and of course, I was active from the get-go, putting dishes away, reaching for things, and doing as much as I could within reason.

Sarah was such a help with the drains. We would turn on "Ooh Child" from the *Guardians of the Galaxy* soundtrack, sing the lyrics together, and just get it done. We'd sing about how things were going to get better, as Sarah measured.

To get my hair washed, Sarah would drive me to a nearby Great Clips, and eventually I drove myself, although I probably drove too early. But oh, it felt so good to get my hair washed! I told one of the ladies there about my surgery, and she shared that her mom was also a breast cancer survivor and had had a double mastectomy, too. She was so sweet and supportive— another "God appointment."

I spent the next several weeks at home recovering. That winter, it was chilly but not too cold, and when it was sunny, I'd go on the back patio and soak up the sun.

For so many years, I had felt like a hamster on a wheel. All I did was work, and I never felt I had have enough time to be alone with God, or time to take care of myself, or even just time to do nothing. Now I could finally just breathe, and it felt awesome. It gave me a real reason to heal.

When it came to my after-surgery treatment plan, I quickly learned how to be my own advocate. I went with what my intuition told me. I asked questions and did some research, but I did not overly research things. I trusted the guidance of my close friends who had also gone through cancer. Their experience was invaluable. But ultimately it was my journey and my decisions.

My treatment wasn't the only part of my plan. I changed what I ate fairly early on in the journey. I made better nutritional choices for myself, such as choosing organic fruits and vegetables, limiting my intake of processed foods, and limiting alcohol.

Mindfulness became very important to me. I started practicing meditation after my cancer diagnosis, and I still do it daily. I love the Insight Timer app, which includes ten-day courses that I've found beneficial. I also listen to music in healing frequencies like 432

Now I could finally just breathe, and it felt awesome.

Hz, 528 Hz, etc. (If you haven't heard of healing frequencies, Google it!)

I discovered restorative yoga after my diagnosis, as well as lymphatic massage. All of these practices felt calming and nurturing, and they helped heal my body and soul.

Trust your intuition. Research, ask questions, but don't obsess. Staying in the moment can help ease any anxiety you may be feeling. Explore the benefits of meditation, music, yoga, and massage. Breathwork also can help immensely. Make a plan, but also be prepared for the plan to change.

What is your treatment plan? What practices will you add to your plan that feel nurturing to your body and soul?

_____

_____

_____

_____

CHAPTER 4

BELIEVE IN YOURSELF

Celebrate your life, you are your own light.

LAILAH GIFTY AKITA

J ust when I felt like I could breathe again, I had an appointment with Dr. Rush to talk about whether I had uterine cancer and would need a hysterectomy.

Based on the cells he retrieved, Dr. Rush said that 50 percent of pathologists would say I had cancer, and 50 percent would say I didn't.

"So, it's really up to you," he concluded.

I had to make the decision?

My biggest concern, as usual, was missing as little work as possible. So, I thought, *I'm off work now. No better time, right?* After all, the fibroids were heavy and uncomfortable.

I decided to have the surgery. They scheduled it for February 3.

I had the most awesome gynecological oncologist: Dr. Stickles. She was a relatively young woman but very experienced, super intelligent, and really good at what she did. This surgery worried me more than anything. I met with Dr. Stickles a couple times to talk about what would happen afterward, particularly about how the hysterectomy would affect my sexuality. I was relieved to find out it likely wouldn't have a significant effect.

Another anesthesiologist told me to count backward from ten to one. Another stay at Vanderbilt, this one longer . . .

Immediately after the hysterectomy, they tested the tumor for cancer. Not long after they transferred me from recovery to my hospital room, with my family standing around me, Dr. Stickles came into my room and announced that I did not have cancer. We all started cheering and celebrating.

Two days later, I was resting alone in my room, looking forward to going home. Dr. Stickles suddenly walked in with about six other people—doctors in training and medical students. They all stood in a semicircle around my bed while Dr. Stickles explained that I did, in fact, have cancer.

"What?" was all I could ask. (Plunging roller coaster . . .)

"I'm going to meet with the tumor board to determine what kind of tumor it is and whether you need to have lymph nodes taken out of your legs . . ."

I didn't hear much after that.

I stayed in the hospital for four days. I had a few visitors during that time. One of my pastors came to see me, and one of my friends from church brought me a book, which was really sweet. I was up and walking around pretty quickly, so the doctors let me go home a day early. I know, overachiever . . . smile.

The following week, the tumor board met and determined the cancer was just in the lining of my uterus and hadn't spread anywhere else. That meant the lymph nodes in my legs did not need to be removed. And no chemo so far.

Cancer-Free and Reconstruction

During the surgery, they had removed not only my uterus and ovaries but also my cervix. I'm not sure why they did that, although Dr. Stickles told me at one point that it had been a little touch and go because I had three huge fibroids, and one of them was near a major blood vessel.

The important thing was that they got all the cancer.

I ended up being out of work for six weeks. I used all of my short-term disability, my family medical leave, and everything else I had available. By mid-February, ready or not, it was time to go back to work.

I was still recovering from two major surgeries, and I noticed that I couldn't think straight at work. It was just the most mind-boggling time. Yesterday, a friend and I were talking about this period in my life, and she told me, "You're a very strong person."

I thought, *What's the alternative?* The way I saw it, I was forced to rise to the occasion, whether I wanted to or not.

Meanwhile, I was preparing for the breast reconstruction surgery. Every week I went to Dr. Higdon's office, where they gradually filled the tissue expanders. They also worked on releasing the scar tissue (which felt like a tight band around my chest) with a special kind of massage. Once the tissue expanders were the right size, the reconstruction surgery would happen.

I view reconstruction as a very personal decision. Before cancer, I would have never considered implants, but after a double mastectomy, I knew that's what I wanted. To me, it was part of my path toward feeling whole.

I've found that it's best not to give people advice about reconstruction or any other cancer-related decisions. Just share your experience and encourage them to make their own decision. You never know how you'll feel when you're in that situation or what will be important to you.

The week before my reconstruction surgery, my boyfriend took me out to Kayne Prime, a really nice steak restaurant in Nashville. Part of the reason I wanted to go was that I was really scared. *Rather than waiting until after the surgery to celebrate,* I thought, *let's celebrate now, in case something happens to me.*

We had a lovely dinner. Kayne Prime is known for putting all sorts of interesting ingredients together resulting in such delicious food.

Just share your experience and encourage them to make their own decision. You never know how you'll feel when you're in that situation or what will be important to you.

At the end of the meal, we realized that our bill was going to be at least three hundred dollars. The server laid the leather folder on the table. We opened it and saw a handwritten note: "Congratulations on beating breast cancer! The meal's on us."

To me, this was another God wink. It was going to be OK.

Reconstruction was a tough surgery. In some ways it still feels like a blur. I don't remember a lot of specifics about it. I was really bruised and sore afterward, but it also felt like my femininity was intact again. Everyone feels differently about this, but for me it meant so much to have a sense of wholeness again.

Celebrating Being a Survivor

How appropriate that October is Breast Cancer Awareness Month—and also the month of the Susan G. Komen race. That year, I decided to go.

Just as my friend Tracie had encouraged me to do, I stopped by the survivors' breakfast tent first. I was happy to see that it was sponsored by none other than J. Christopher's—my favorite breakfast place in Franklin,

Tennessee. I showed them my race registration, and although everyone gets a t-shirt, the survivors get one that says "survivor." I also got my wristband and my survivor sticker. That tiny pink sticker means a lot to me—I collect one for each year cancer-free. I could have reached out to Tracie and gone with her, but Sarah and I went together; Liz had to work that day.

As I sat down to breakfast, I was surprised at how special it felt to be celebrated for surviving breast cancer. It all felt so emotional and personal.

After breakfast, I walked around the vendor booths, which were all arranged in a circle. It was like Halloween: vendors like McDonald's and Dunkin' Donuts and various hospitals were handing out bags of goodies, including food, buttons, backpacks, bracelets, and bottles of hand sanitizer. As I watched the people around me, I could tell the participants had been meeting there for years.

Before the actual race began, some survivors got onstage and danced to Zumba-type music. Then everyone began to line up for the survivors' parade behind different signs based on how long they had survived cancer: zero to five years, five years, ten years, twenty-five years. I walked over and stood behind the zero to five year sign, the music began, and we all marched out while people cheered and took pictures.

Standing under the zero to five year sign, I felt like I was just beginning my survivor journey; it was overwhelmingly emotional. The other women and I cried and hugged and cheered one another on as we walked. We were survivors!

After the parade, it was time for the race, beginning with the 5K. I decided to do the one-mile walk. It was fun because I ended up talking to other walkers and getting to know other survivors. Sarah walked with me, and we enjoyed the fresh autumn air and the camaraderie.

I saw seasoned runners, women wearing little knit hats who were obviously going through chemo, and everyone in between. Many people were part of teams dressed all in pink, in tutus, or in other creative costumes. A lot of people walked with their dogs. One lady with a walker brought her little dog dressed in a little costume.

When we got to the finish line, crowds of people were cheering and music was playing, but I noticed they didn't take pictures or give medals like they do at other races. I wondered about that, but then I learned it was because they wanted to give as much money as possible to cancer research.

That's when I realized what was so powerful about the Susan G. Komen race. Each year, we have special celebrations—Thanksgiving, Christmas, birthdays, etc. I realized how important it is to celebrate surviving breast cancer every year, too, in such an upbeat way.

As I've learned in cancer as well as in life: Trust your intuition and believe in yourself. If you don't believe in yourself, no one else will. However, believing in yourself doesn't mean you don't need support. I'm sure it would have been easier for me to go through all of this with a partner or spouse. I had no one to fall back on financially. I'll be honest, that was tough. Then, coming out of it all and trying to process it and be authentic and true to myself— I'm not going to lie—it was tough. I hired a great therapist, and we worked for more than three years processing the whole thing. She often reminded me of how strong I was, and her support was priceless. She recommended so many

I realized how important

it is to celebrate surviving

breast cancer every year.

books; Broken Open *by Elizabeth Lesser and* The Book of Awakening *by Mark Nepo are two that I still reread to this day. Seeking therapy was one of the best things I did for myself. I looked forward to our weekly appointments.*

If you are married, be transparent with your spouse about what you need to keep believing in yourself. Maybe you need time to process what's happening. Some people like to stay busy at work, and that helps them. Just be honest with yourself every step of the way.

How can you believe in yourself today?

_____

_____

_____

_____

What kind of support do you need? What serves you?

_____

_____

_____

_____

CHAPTER 5

HAVE FAITH

When you get into a tight place and
everything goes against you, till it seems
as though you could not hang on a minute
longer, never give up then, for that is just
the place and time that the tide will turn.

HARRIET BEECHER STOWE

I really took the mindset of the Susan G. Komen race to heart. I had just had what I believed to be my final cancer surgery. I needed to celebrate!

One of the items on my bucket list was to go to New York and see *Saturday Night Live*. I had been to the city once in the 1980s, and then only briefly.

The only problem was that it was really hard to get tickets to SNL. The typical way is to enter a lottery, and only a few people win each week. The other option is to wait in line for hours overnight in the cold.

Sarah loves SNL too, so she did some research. It turned out that if you had been through extraordinary circumstances, you could request tickets from a producer. Sarah networked her way to that producer through LinkedIn and sent her an email saying I had just been through cancer and would love to see *Saturday Night Live*. I also called and left the producer a voicemail. We were ecstatic when we received a phone call saying we got tickets, and they ended up being great seats, which was really sweet of them.

So, just before Thanksgiving, Sarah and I took a weekend trip to New York.

The night of the show, we climbed up the huge staircase at the iconic 30 Rock and waited in line to get in. The walls were lined with photos of SNL alums, including Gilda Radner, a hero of mine. We struck up a conversation with the couple next to us, who said they attended every year because they knew the producer. They showed us the ropes, and we learned that there weren't many seats—the young people were sitting in seats on the floor, while we would be seated in the balcony. While we were standing in line, we got to meet the producer who gave us the tickets and were able to thank her personally.

The show was hosted by Elizabeth Banks from *The Hunger Games,* and the musical guests were Sam Smith and Lorde. The band was amazing, and what stood out to me most was seeing the whole production come together. It was so electrifying. By the way, they don't use canned laughter; the laughter is live, so when we watch a recording of the show, you can actually hear us laughing— because it was so funny! It was a perfect evening.

Throughout the weekend, we didn't have a plan; we just let ourselves explore. We went to the top of the Empire State Building, which I'd never done before, and it was breathtaking. It also was *really* cold. We visited the New York Library, and we walked as far as our feet would take us.

As we were walking by Rockefeller Center, we saw St. Patrick's Cathedral, a huge Catholic church where different Catholic bishops are buried. We aren't Catholic,

Throughout the weekend,

we didn't have a plan;

we just let ourselves explore.

but I felt drawn to enter. We walked around inside for a bit, and then we noticed people beginning to gather. Being a very curious person, I asked a woman, "What's going on?"

We learned they were getting ready for a Mass held by a group called the Sovereign Military Hospitaller Order of Saint John of Jerusalem, of Rhodes, and of Malta, a healing ministry that travels around the world to pray for people.

"Oh, you should stay," said the woman, whose name was Mary.

"Well, I don't know . . ." I said, uncertain.

Then suddenly, I *was* certain. I turned to Sarah. "Oh, Sarah, we should stay; it sounds really interesting."

Sarah rolled her eyes. "No, Mom, we're in New York; we should be shopping or walking around and seeing things, not going to church."

"I feel like we're supposed to be here," I insisted.

We stayed.

During the Mass, one of the priests walked around and asked for people who needed healing to stand up and receive a laying on of hands and anointing with oil.

Mary, who was sitting next to me, instantly said, "You should stand up and get prayed for."

I was a little bit hesitant. I wasn't Catholic, I was a guest here, and this was their Mass. Who was I to ask for prayer? Even so, I got up and stood in the aisle, and the priest came and prayed over me.

In that moment, I received a deep sense of healing. The surgeons had said they got all the cancer, but maybe they didn't—who knows? Somehow I knew I was healed, with those welcoming people in that peaceful, beautiful place. As we were leaving, they gave us an ornament, which I put on my tree every year.

Another God appointment.

Brain Fog and Burnout

Meanwhile, I'd been doing the best I could to keep my job at HealthStream, even though my mind was very distant from what I was doing. I felt very burned out. For one thing, I felt physically trapped in the office, and I wondered if I could be experiencing PTSD from all those surgeries. I had heard that having multiple surgeries in a row can be traumatic, and I had had five in the span of less than a year.

I'd been doing so well at HealthStream prior to being sick. On a scale from zero to fifteen, I had been a fifteen in my career there, and now I felt like a three. Not only were my numbers dropping; my heart just wasn't in it to turn things around.

It might have been all the anesthesia and all the trauma. It might have been the Tamoxifen. It might have been being thrown into menopause after the hysterectomy. Maybe it was everything combined. All I knew was that I was in a high-stakes, fast-paced sales position, and I felt constantly confused. I was nowhere close to getting my life back, and I didn't know where to go from there.

But really, none of that mattered. I just needed to keep showing up. People were depending on me.

I was getting ready to do a webinar to close a really nice deal with a company on the East Coast. This webinar was one of a series of conversations I had been having with a group of women who had been in credentialing for years and had been tracking their information manually with spreadsheets. Our software was just phenomenal, and I knew it would help them greatly. During the webinar, I would be demonstrating the software to both the users and the decision makers.

The webinar would include several people in different time zones, so there were a lot of pieces to put together. Normally, of course, it wouldn't be that big of a deal. I had gotten everyone online and was setting up the software on my laptop so I could share my screen with them, but for some reason I just couldn't get it to work. Part of it probably was due to technical difficulties, but part of it was also that my brain just couldn't process things the way it used to. My emotions were going haywire, and I could barely hold it together.

It was a $50,000 deal. But I finally had to say, "Ladies, I'm so sorry. I need to reschedule. I apologize."

I felt so humiliated and embarrassed and out of control. I couldn't even pull together a sales meeting, and that scared me. I couldn't do my job anymore. If I couldn't do my job, what would become of me?

We did end up rescheduling, and I was able to close that deal. Thank goodness I did! That deal would be my last at HealthStream.

After Thanksgiving, my boss and I mutually decided I would leave at the end of the year. He was kind enough to let me work from home until then, and I was very thankful he was sensitive to how I was feeling.

I felt like leaving was the right decision. Part of me was scared about my future, but part of me was excited.

A Christmas to Celebrate

We stayed home for Christmas that year. The previous year, when I was going through treatment, I had bought this tiny little tree at Whole Foods, put it in the middle of my kitchen table, and decided it would have to be enough. But I also couldn't help stopping by the Christmas tree farm they set up every year by Walgreens, just to look around. I picked out a natural wreath to put on my door, and I ended up talking to a guy who worked there named Terry. I told him what I was going through, and he said, "The Lord won't give you more than you can handle." Terry's words meant a lot to me.

"I'll see you next year," I said, my voice quivering. And I meant it.

So, this Christmas, I went back to the tree farm, and I brought Sarah with me.

I saw Terry and walked right up to him.

"Terry, I made it," I said. "I had five surgeries, but I'm still here. I made it." We hugged.

Then Sarah and I started looking at trees. Usually I just buy a twenty-five-dollar tree at Lowe's or Home Depot. This year was going to be different.

We chose a beautiful, full, ten-foot tree. Terry helped us load it onto our truck, and we brought it home.

After we got the tree set up, I pulled out all my ornaments. I have a lot of beautiful ornaments; every year, I have a tradition of buying each of my girls an ornament with the year on it so that when they have their own homes, they will have a beautiful tree reminding them of their childhood. We decorated the tree with all those ornaments. To me, it was breathtaking.

During that Christmas season, I went bowling one night. I wore my compression sleeves to protect my arms from lymphedema. I walked confidently up to the lane with my bowling stance and threw with as much power as I could muster. Roll, roll, roll, and . . . gutter. What? Why was this happening? Again, walk, one, two, throw . . . gutter. I was embarrassed and humiliated. I couldn't get my body to remember how to throw the ball. But I had a strong feeling that I wanted to figure this out.

A week later, I went to a local bowling alley to buy a ball. I got a custom-made ball, with my own holes drilled to fit my grip. The guy behind the counter gave me pointers—he'd worked there for years—and I knocked down some pins with his instruction. I was really proud of myself.

If I had given up bowling after that embarrassing night, it would have been a mistake. I felt so empowered to have my own ball—one I could throw—and my own bag to keep it in. Before long, I was back to playing the way I used to play.

No, I didn't jump out of a plane like President Bush did on his ninetieth birthday. But I did decide I was going to bowl again. I pushed through my fears and physical changes, and I learned to bowl again!

No, I didn't jump out of
a plane like President
Bush did on his ninetieth
birthday. But I did decide
I was going to bowl again.

Reconstructing My Life

My job with HealthStream would end January 1. The reality of needing to find work fast sunk in. I sat on my couch and cried out, "God, what am I supposed to do with my life now?" I was frustrated, confused, and a little hopeless.

I finally decided to reach out to companies that sell software for nonprofits; putting together my sales skills with my desire to work with a nonprofit seemed to make sense. I began reaching out to every job opportunity I could think of. I paid a company to redo my resume and help me with my LinkedIn profile to make me really marketable, and they did a great job. I sent my resume to probably one hundred different companies on LinkedIn. I constantly asked, "God, how do you want me to spend my life?" I began to feel hopeful that God might have something for me—even with all the disappointments.

A company called Gift Clarity invited me to come in to interview for a straight commission sales job. They created software for nonprofits, so it seemed like a great fit—I really have a heart for nonprofits, and I've volunteered with several over the years. My figure had completely changed since the cancer surgeries, so I went out and bought a new suit for the interview.

The day of the interview, I felt excited but also very overwhelmed. I'm a very determined person, and I typically just put one foot in front of the other, put on my game face, and be strong. That day, I put on my new suit and got ready to go—and almost had a panic attack as I was leaving the house.

What am I doing? I kept thinking. *I'm not ready for this.*

I overcame the panic attack, made it to the interview, and got the job. I began work on a trial basis. But I soon realized it wasn't going to bring in income quickly enough.

The team was spread out all over the country, and I didn't feel there was enough support for what I needed at the time. So, I decided not to continue with that job, even though they really liked me. I kept looking.

I got another interview with a semi-startup software company and had a great meeting with the CEO and founder. He was so positive. The company had just hired a sales manager, and we had a phone interview, but he kept putting me off. Finally he sent me an email that seemed to list all the reasons he should have hired me, but he never offered me a job. That was really disappointing.

If I had wondered before, now I knew for sure: As a single mother in her fifties recovering from cancer, I was at a major disadvantage, especially at most software firms where the salespeople are typically in their thirties or early forties at most.

I prayed. I sent out more resumes. I talked to everyone I knew about job opportunities. I looked into temp work. I even got certified as a life coach.

You name it, I was doing it.

Well, God, I'm still alive. It looks like I made it. Now what?

That's when I realized the surgeries were only the beginning of my cancer journey. I had reconstructed my body. How was I going to reconstruct my life?

I have attended several churches through the years, and I've had a relationship with God all my life. Cancer made me realize I needed to develop my faith even more. I had to dig deep into what I believed. Not what my ex-husband or my boyfriend believed, but what I believed. I think that's always evolving to some degree,

Cancer made me realize
I needed to develop my faith
even more. I had to dig
deep into what I believed.

but this journey also showed me that my faith was mine and mine alone. I didn't have to follow someone else; instead, I had to contemplate where *I* stood.

As a cancer survivor, you will grieve your past life to some degree. Allow yourself to do it. Your past body, your past feelings of health security, your past job, your past hopes and dreams. But you will come out of it a better person. A deeper person, a more hopeful and joyous person with new goals and new hopes and new dreams. You will be a light to everyone around you. You will inspire others with your life. It's an amazing thing—your story makes a difference; it matters. Have faith that you are worthy of a new beginning.

What do you have faith in?

_____

_____

_____

_____

CHAPTER 6

NEW BEGINNINGS

Right now, you are one choice
away from a new beginning.

OPRAH

In February, we heard that Al Roker and Hoda Kotb were coming to Nashville to do book signings. I watch the *Today* show every day; I just love them. "Oh, we should go!" Sarah said.

The first day, we went to Al Roker's book signing at Parnassus Books. It was great to give Al a hug and meet his beautiful wife, Deborah. We found out Hoda was speaking at the Nashville Public Library the next day, and luckily we were able to attend. When I had been stuck at home, recovering from various surgeries, I had always watched Hoda and Kathie Lee (now Jenna), and if I couldn't see it, I recorded it to watch later. It was my connection to the world and gave me a lot of peace. I knew that Hoda had survived breast cancer, and I noticed that for years, she always wore a pink hope ring on her index finger.

At the library, Hoda told her story about how, at the beginning of her career, she drove around to twenty-seven different news stations and was turned down at every single one. This was before GPS or smartphone navigation, so on her way home she somehow got turned around and ended up in Mississippi before she realized what had happened. She stopped in a town to use the restroom and happened to see a news station. She walked in, they hired her on the spot, and the rest was history. I really took that story to heart: Hoda never gave up. She persevered. Just like I was trying to do.

At the end, there was a time to ask questions, and I raised my hand. I don't remember exactly what I said, but I started telling her that I had gone through cancer, too.

She came down off the stage and walked right up to me.

"Can I give you a hug?" she asked.

It was the most wonderful hug. I felt so encouraged. Afterward, Sarah and I stood in line for the book signing.

When it was our turn to get our book signed and we were talking to her at the table, I saw she was wearing that pink hope ring.

"I love that ring," I said. "Where'd you get it? I'd love to get one."

"Oh, have mine," she said. She slipped it off and handed it to me. I couldn't believe it! Seeing her wear that ring had meant so much to me, and now she was giving it to me.

I keep it in my jewelry box because I don't want to wear it out, but on very special occasions, especially during that year, I wear it. When I do, I look at it and remember that Hoda persevered, and I can too. Having that ring when I had no idea what I was going to do with my life, overwhelmed as a single woman in her fifties, made such a difference at such an uncertain time.

Hidden Gifts

I had also discovered a hidden gift in my unemployment: I finally had time to do what I never made time to do before. After my surgeries, I had trouble making my bed. I was determined to get my strength back. I reached and stretched as much as I could within reason. I went to the local Y and worked with a trainer named David, and he helped me get my strength back. My body felt so foreign to me. I did some physical therapy with Cindy's friend Wiley, who owned a Tae Kwon Do studio and also happened to be an ex-nurse. I also got a lymphatic drainage massage every month with Tina, who I met at Vanderbilt.

It took a good three years to settle into my new body and have it feel like my own again. If I had had a full-time job, I can virtually guarantee I wouldn't have taken the time to do all that. But because I did, as of today, I've finally got my strength back.

I was also learning to dream again.

For some reason, during that time, I knew I needed to immediately start doing the things I needed to do. Going to New York was one of them. Another was writing this book: from the moment I was diagnosed,

I discovered a hidden gift in my unemployment: I finally had time to do what I never made time to do before.

I started keeping a journal so I would remember all the parts of my story I wanted to share with others going through cancer after I had gotten through it myself. I had no idea how to write or publish a book, but I just recorded my story.

Another one of my dreams was to travel. I kept my eyes open for opportunities we could afford on a budget, and that's when I heard about a school trip Sarah's French teacher organizes almost every year. That year they were doing a whirlwind tour of Paris, Nice, Pisa, Florence, and Rome over the course of nine days. The school group was part of a bigger group of students from all over the country, and Sarah's school could take seven students.

Three of Sarah's best friends were going, and of course Sarah said she *needed* to go. Then one of the teachers couldn't go, and they needed a chaperone. The price was very reasonable. *Hmm.*

The Trip of a Lifetime

Not only was the trip a win-win—it was a no-brainer. I had wanted to travel abroad since college. A lot of my friends had done study abroad programs, but I never had. Honestly, it was a dream come true. And it was another thing that probably never would have happened if I had been working full time.

I applied for my passport, and I kept working with David and Wiley to increase my endurance and get ready for the trip of a lifetime.

Sarah and I went to Europe in June 2016, and it truly was a whirlwind. Seeing the Eiffel Tower, the Sistine Chapel, and the Vatican—talk about taking my breath away. Each of those experiences was like stepping into heaven.

When we arrived the first day, we were told that staying up the first night and waking up at local time was the best way to get over the jet lag, so that's what we did. Our first morning, we stumbled around Paris exhausted and exhilarated all at once.

Flowers were in full bloom everywhere. I couldn't stop thinking about how much my mother would have loved France. I couldn't bring her flowers, so instead I bought her some macaroons—which was a sign I wasn't thinking straight, because macaroons are almost as perishable as flowers. They came in a rainbow of colors: pink, mint green, chocolate . . . they were beautiful.

That day also happened to be the day of a big European soccer match, and France had just won the playoffs. When we exited the Eiffel Tower, we were met with a wall of singing, shouting, and drinking soccer fans. It was mass chaos, like something out of a movie, and police were everywhere. At that moment, the sky opened up, and it started pouring rain, which ended up being kind of a blessing because the throng parted as people ran for the eaves, awnings, and any shelter they could find.

Our feisty Italian tour guide led our group of thirty through the street so fast that we didn't even have time to open an umbrella. We were booking it to get to the downtown train, and so many people were trying to get through that we were like one massive person moving together. To avoid injury, the station finally opened up the turnstiles, which meant we could get on the train without needing to pay.

Sarah was carrying the macaroons in a paper bag, which was beyond soaked at that point. As she went through the turnstile, all of those beautiful cookies fell to the ground. Right there, at that moment, I broke down. It was so embarrassing. A French guy leaned over and tried to get them and hand them to me, while I just kept sobbing.

Obviously, I wasn't emotionally healed yet. I was overcome by an immense amount of guilt: My mom was never going to go to France, and the one thing I was going to bring her was destroyed. But the truth was they had already gotten stale. I guess my lack of sleep wasn't a good thing.

We spent two days in Paris, and then took the high-speed train to Nice. I took lots of pictures of the beach, which consisted of pebbles rather than sand. As we were walking down the street by the beach, I felt a sense of peace.

The next day was Monaco, then on to Pisa, Italy. And then we visited Rome. We traveled by bus during this leg of the trip.

On our last day, we saw the Vatican, the Vatican Museum, the Sistine Chapel, and the Coliseum. By that time, I was exhausted, and although I hated to do it, I asked if there was any way I could leave. I just couldn't stand up any longer. Our tour guide said sure, so I got in a taxi by myself and went to the hotel. An hour later our little group cut it short and came home, too.

Sarah was so sweet; the whole time she had to carry my bags because I really wasn't up to it. Sometimes she got very frustrated that she was stuck helping her mom instead of walking with her friends, but later she apologized. We were both so thankful we took that trip together.

The Importance of Beauty

In Versailles, I bought myself a beautiful scarf in a gift shop. It was made of very thin material and was very artistic looking, so rather than wearing it, I decided to frame it and put it over my bed. Every time I see it, it reminds me that God wants me to have beauty in my life.

Being raised by a single mother, the message I received as a child was that I needed to learn to make do with what I had. Over time, I interpreted that to mean I didn't deserve to feel joy or have beautiful things. The day I hung that scarf over my bed, I made a decision: It was time for me to have more beautiful things in my life.

Every time I see the scarf, it reminds me that God wants me to have beauty in my life.

I consciously changed the hardware on my kitchen cabinets, my doorknobs, and my light fixtures. I painted my bedroom sea salt, a beautiful, restful, heavenly color I loved. Now everywhere I looked, I saw something beautiful.

By choosing to surround myself with beauty, I began to believe I deserved it. I began to believe I could create a peaceful life for myself, one small step at a time.

I felt a truth begin to well up from within my soul: *God wants us to have a beautiful environment that speaks to our souls and gives us rest and peace.* No matter where I lived, how much money I had, or with whom I lived, my home could become a sanctuary—a place of peace and quiet and communion with God and those I loved.

Looking back, getting back in shape, traveling, getting a life coaching certification, and refining my environment were all healing practices for me. And even though I couldn't find a job and my mom's health was spinning out of control, having a list of to-dos helped me feel that I was moving forward and not just sitting around watching TV; that list kept me from feeling stuck. My friend Tracie was right: It's so important to have a plan. Of course, we're never going to finish all the tasks, but a to-do list reminds you that you've got a life; you've got stuff to do. Goals push me forward.

An Empty-Nester

My next goal was getting Sarah moved to Columbia College in Chicago.

Taking Sarah to Chicago was an adventure in and of itself. We took a road trip to Michigan to see relatives beforehand and most of the trip we talked about everything. Sarah was a good listener and so mature for her age. As we pulled into Chicago, the reality of leaving her in a big city alone and going home to an empty house filled my mind. I tried to hold in my emotions because I didn't want her to feel guilty for pursuing her dreams and doing what was natural and normal at her age. I didn't want her to worry about me, and I wanted her move-in day to be fun and exciting!

Well . . . when we arrived at her dorm, there was a system for parents to use a large cardboard box on wheels to transport the belongings up to the room. We found one, rolled it to my car, and started filling it up. Up to this point, we were OK, but as we tried to roll it, the large box kept sliding off the frame, and we couldn't maneuver it very well.

All I could see for blocks were other dads helping their children on this important day. One of the dads finally helped us steady the box and get it to her floor. Another dad helped us load the second and third box, and another helped move the heavy furniture in the dorm room. I was very thankful for the help of strangers.

After all the work was done, I headed to an empty hotel room before my drive back the next day—eleven hours alone. I didn't even have my beloved pet Miles anymore because we had to put him to sleep right before leaving for Chicago. I was going home to a new life. No more lacrosse games, sleepovers, or school projects. My years of being a single parent for the most part were over. Another thing to grieve—another letting go.

A Mission Trip

A few months later, I was sitting in a meeting to learn more about a mission trip to Malawi, Africa. It wasn't the first time I had sat in this meeting. Seventeen years ago, I had heard the same presentation.

My years of being a
single parent for the most
part were over. Another
thing to grieve—
another letting go.

This time, I was going. Now that I truly had an empty nest, I decided to take advantage of it. I just happened to receive a check in the mail that was nearly the exact amount I needed, which I viewed as confirmation. I began preparing for the trip. I had a lot to do:

- Get a series of different kinds of immunizations
- Fill my anti-malaria medicine prescription to take with me, just in case
- Gather all the items I would need to travel to a remote area of Africa

In October 2017, I spent two and a half weeks working with the Duwa Project in Malawi, Africa. My friend Morgan had started this project when she was getting her master's degree, and it helps women create their own business by making crafts, like placemats and Christmas ornaments. Morgan teaches them all the details of running a profitable business: how to decide what products to make, know what supplies they need, and how to save and invest their money, all as a team.

We got to see firsthand the difference this extra money has made for them. One woman told us she was able to build a home and rent it out, and another said that her child was able to receive malaria treatment. It was wonderful to watch the women working together and see grassroots business development in Malawi.

Going to another country is wonderful but also jarring. On one hand, I realized how much we have in the United States; on the other, I realized how happy people can be without many of the things we have. For example, we visited Kauma Village, a slum settlement of 45,000 people. The name means "dried up" or "no hope" because of the lack of resources. The people live in severe poverty and lack adequate housing and clean water. But what I remember most was its beauty.

The open-air market had fresh fish, meat, sweet potatoes, little handmade brooms, brightly colored cloth—table after table of everything you can imagine. People were dressed in the most beautiful colors. Many of the little children had never seen a person with light skin before; they would run up to us, even though we could tell they were scared. All the people I encountered seemed so peaceful. They seemed more joyous, less burdened.

Malawi is a beautiful country. We got to go on a safari the last couple days, and on our way down the river, an elephant walked right in front of us. About two hundred hippopotamuses were swimming in the river. Our flat-bottomed boat could have been turned over by just one of those giant creatures. I couldn't even begin to count the beautiful birds I saw. It was amazing. The sun was going down, and the entire scene was breathtaking. I was a little sad when my seventeen-year dream was almost over. My heart was so full.

On our last day, during breakfast, I happened to sit next to a cancer researcher based in Africa. For the past year, I had been bothered by the skin around my eyes, which had become strangely thick and droopy. I had been off the Tamoxifen for months (my choice), and I wasn't on any other drugs, so I had no idea what was causing it. I had been to several dermatologists, a general physician, and an ophthalmologist, and no one had been able to help me. I had a bag of creams, and none of them worked. It was very disheartening, not just because I felt self-conscious in general, but because it affected the way I showed up during job interviews.

I decided to ask the cancer researcher about my eyes. He told me it was likely a side effect of the drugs I had taken, and they don't know why it happens, but it happens. Strangely enough, soon after I got home from Africa, it went away on its own.

New Job—New Life

One afternoon, I was on Indeed and saw an ad for a part-time job in community engagement with a nonprofit called Renewal House. At the interview, I had an instant connection with the director of development, Lis. She had years of experience in the nonprofit world, and I loved her enthusiasm and gusto. She was the real deal. I knew I was perfect for the job—coupling my cold calling experience with my love of helping people and desire to make a difference. Luckily, she thought so too, and she hired me.

Sarah was in college. And now I could put my nose to the grindstone and live fully in my new life.

Are you caring for others more than you care for yourself? Are you watching others live the life you wish you were living? Watch for the things that make you happy and bring a smile to your face and do more of them. Some ideas:

- ❈ *Buy yourself fresh flowers*
- ❈ *Plan that trip you've put off*
- ❈ *Redecorate your space*
- ❈ *Start a new hobby you always wanted to try*

What items are still on your bucket list? Go do one. Fill your thoughts with happy thoughts. Focus on life.

What one thing will you do today that brings you joy?

_____

_____

_____

_____

CHAPTER 7

FIRING ON ALL CYLINDERS

Your work is going to fill a large part of your life, and the only way to be truly satisfied is to do what you believe is great work. And the only way to do great work is to love what you do.

STEVE JOBS

My job at Renewal House seemed perfect. I loved giving presentations to companies all around Nashville to help promote the awesome work Renewal House was doing with women addicted to opioids and their children.

But eventually I started to feel trapped again. The commute took at least an hour each way. When I finally arrived, I had to sit in an old, dusty office with bars on the windows. I even offered to paint my office and bring in a standing desk and some artwork. They wouldn't allow that, however. Even though I could do everything I needed to from home, no one was allowed to work from home.

I hated being cooped up in an office. It just didn't make me happy. I began to dread every day, and I knew I didn't want to feel that way about my work. I really wanted meaningful work—especially after surviving cancer. Yet here I was, stuck in an office once again, and I didn't like it at all. When I left to do presentations, that part was fulfilling. Knowing I was helping the work of Renewal House was also fulfilling.

When I considered leaving, though, I didn't feel much better. *How would I support myself? How would I find a job that didn't make me feel like I was a prisoner? Why did I think I deserved more? Shouldn't I just be glad I had a paycheck?*

I hung in there as long as I could. But after seven months, the grant supporting my position was expiring,

I began to dread every day,
and I knew I didn't want to
feel that way about my work.

and I had the hard conversation with my boss letting her know that I wanted to move on.

Starting My Own Business

I'd always been very entrepreneurial, so I brainstormed ideas for my very own business. Surely I could take all my business skills and start my own small business. I dove into research: I watched videos, read books and articles, and took lots of notes. After exploring many options, I decided to start a pressure washing company for residential and commercial customers. I loved all the research—and there was a lot. I researched ways to clean, ways to run the business, the best equipment, the best cleaners to use for what, and so on. With my years of sales and business experience, I had a lot of fun putting it together. I obtained the business licenses and insurance. I put an ad on Indeed and received fifty-six resumes. I pored over the resumes and chose fifteen people to contact. After all those interviews, I chose one man to work as a contractor: Opey.

Opey was such a blessing. He was a hard worker and had a great attitude. For the early jobs, I held his ladder and helped as much as I could. I took great pride in the job we did, and so did he. I set up a Facebook page and posted pictures of our work. It was such a joy to start something from scratch.

One day, Opey and I were power washing a home in an upscale neighborhood. Across the street, a group of women were sitting on their front porches watching us intently and clearly talking about us. Next, the woman we were working for came out and told us they were calling her and asking why it was taking us so long.

None of their business, I thought. Opey did very thorough work. He was meticulous and paid attention to detail. Their rudeness didn't faze him a bit.

But it made me nervous. I had to admit the business wasn't going the way I thought it would. I was anxious about my future. I didn't have a feeling of peace. I knew I needed to land on my feet and support myself, and instead I was floundering.

A New Opportunity

One day, I was sitting in a beautiful real estate office lined with pictures of the Nashville skyline, talking to a young Realtor about using my company to clean houses before being put on the market. It was my one last stab at making Music City Power Wash work.

"You'd make a great Realtor, Heather," she said. "Have you ever considered it?"

Surprised, I stopped for a moment and then said, "Hmm . . . maybe I will consider that. Where would I begin?"

She told me about a school in Nashville where I could take the pre-license A & B courses. I knew a real estate career wouldn't be easy. It would take ramp-up time. It would take money to invest in signs and marketing efforts. It would take emotional energy to sustain lots of rejection. It would take many hours of work for no money. But when I made a sale, it would be so exciting!

Again, I gave some serious thought to my future. I was fifty-six and had many good years left in my working life. I needed to do something I enjoyed that would also earn me a good living. I decided that I would pursue getting my real estate license.

I signed up for the pre-license courses.

The first day, I arrived early so I could get a good seat. It was a good thing because there were more than sixty people jammed into the small room. I immediately made friends with a few fellow students.

The next two weeks were filled with classes all day and homework from seven to eleven p.m. every night. It was a lot of information, but what I was learning filled me with such excitement. I felt fully alive for the first time in years. I did well on each test, and when I took the state test less than a week later, I passed with flying colors. Finally, something I could dig my teeth into!

Everything fell into place. The brokerage, my headshots, my mentor, the training. It all felt so right. Within months, I had a listing, and I was working with buyers, too! I felt I was really on to something big, like I was in the right place. I was so excited about this new career—my hours were flexible, I didn't have a long commute, and I could use my gifts and talents to help others. I truly felt like I had a viable future.

As a single woman, I knew I needed to figure out how to bring in more income. But as a cancer survivor,

I wanted to do something I truly enjoyed *and* something that was balanced so I didn't get as stressed out as I did before I got sick.

After so many surgeries, I had experienced a lot of brain fog. But now, my brain was firing on all cylinders. I was beginning to feel like my hopeful, happy, purposeful self again.

I think we are all put on this planet for a purpose. Everyone's purpose is different, and that is beautiful. It's your job to discover what makes you fire on all cylinders. After cancer, you will realize that you don't want to allow a lot of time wasters in your life. You typically put your foot down and rally for yourself. You look for things that fill your soul. You know—that feeling of being "in the flow." You know how that feels. It's like water to a garden. It creates the blossoming of all things beautiful in your life. It's a gift.

As a cancer survivor, I
wanted to do something
I truly enjoyed and something
that was balanced.

Where in your life do you feel you're "firing on all cylinders"? How can you do more of that?

_____

_____

_____

_____

CHAPTER 8

LOVE YOURSELF

*Self-care is never a selfish act—it is simply good
stewardship of the only gift I have,
the gift I was put on earth to offer to others.*

PARKER PALMER

I began to tackle my mom's mantra—"It ain't what you like"—head on. Well, it *is* what you like. I began asking myself every day: "Heather, what will make you happy today?" A lot of times what made me happy was taking care of others and making their lives better. Other times it was the simple things in life, like discovering a new drink at Starbucks. Certainly it was my new career endeavors as well.

I began asking myself every day: "Heather, what will make you happy today?"

One day I was lying in bed, looking at the Airbnb app, when I saw a little cottage in Buena Vista, Colorado that was available over Labor Day. That cottage had been booked for months, and someone had just canceled.

Something came over me. I immediately booked it, and began planning my trip to Colorado.

A Trip Down Memory Lane

It had been years since I had seen the Rockies. I had worked out there as a young adult for several summers, plus I had been wanting to visit one of my best friends who had moved to Denver eight years ago.

I flew to Denver, rented a car, and drove two hours to Buena Vista. I couldn't check in until 3:00 p.m., so I drove directly to the A/U Ranches, where I used to work. The dirt road was just the same—bumpy and dusty. My heart started to beat faster as I approached the sign. It felt like a dream. *Was I really here?* So many memories flooded my thoughts. I had spent several summers here.

The main office, or what we called the "Hub," was open and unlocked.

"Hello?" I called, expecting someone to be around the corner. No one was there. I wrote a little note and left my business card so they would know I was up at Round-Up Ranch walking around. I felt so happy to be back.

I drove up the road to the ranch and parked in a lot near Valerie Lodge. There was the deck my friend Allen had built by hand, still looking good after all these years. I walked through the lodge—all the doors were unlocked, as if someone knew I'd be visiting. I looked around and remembered meals and dances and shows we'd done. Plays on the stage, bug juice, and laughter.

In my early twenties, I had found myself here. My strength, my independence. My fearlessness. *How could I have lost that? How could life have changed me so much?* Disappointment and grief and loss had made me forget who I was on some levels. It was still a bit of a struggle at times.

I walked around and sat by the lake. The view was breathtaking. So much of me had begun here in the Collegiate Peak Range. There were so many things I loved to do that I had forgotten about. For so much of my life, I put others first and forgot myself.

I had been a mountaineering counselor. I did things that stretched me. I was brave. I overcame a lot of fears here. I led people on the ropes course thirty feet up in the pines. I took kids caving and rock climbing. I went on hikes in the Rockies. This place had molded me into who I was . . . who I still was.

I glanced up the hill to my cabin. Surely it was locked—but it wasn't. I turned on the light and touched the top bunk that had been mine. If only that young woman had known how life would knock her around, and how she would persevere . . .

I found it interesting that no one was there that day. It gave me the time to walk around and think and take it all in. It was a gift. I sat down under some tall, old pines and just remembered.

After a while, I was ready to go. I signed out at the "Hub" and was on my way, full of gratitude for the gift of memories.

The little cottage was just as cute as the Airbnb pictures. And the view was spectacular. The most interesting surprise was that my host had also worked at the ranches! Amazing!

I settled in, wondering if what I had come to do had been accomplished. Why was I drawn again to this place? Was there something I needed to remember, or something I needed to learn?

At the very least, I had reconnected with my love for the Rockies. I loved the majesty of the mountains and the way everyone was active and in good shape. Buena Vista was full of healthy places to eat. My body responded well to the altitude. It felt at home.

The next day, I drove Independence Pass to Aspen, where I had spent many of my days off. The Pass was exhilarating, although I'll admit that I hadn't remembered the windy curves or the drop-offs without a guard rail.

When I got to the top of the Pass, I hiked the half-mile trail to take in the views at more than 12,000 feet. Neither words nor pictures could do it justice.

I thought about my mother—how she allowed me as a very young adult to drive across the country and spend summers here. She trusted me. She believed in me. I realized what she had done for me by giving me this freedom.

I felt gratitude for God who created the mountains. Only God could make such beauty.

Why was I drawn again
to this place? Was there
something I needed to
remember, or something
I needed to learn?

Fly Fishing and Life Lessons

When I got back, I received another surprise: My host also happened to be a full-time fly-fishing guide. I had always wanted to try fly fishing. What better place than here?

The next morning, we stood knee deep in the Arkansas River at a place called Numbers, apparently because all its rapids are numbered. My feet felt chilled from the cool water, while my soul soared with joy and peace and hope. Water rushed and pooled around us, and every once in a while, a trout jumped. Bubbles cradled the rocks, and the sun reflected and shimmered on the water.

I breathed in the clean mountain air. I felt so alive, so free, so full of everything I was supposed to be. And in the quietness of the graceful cast of the line, I caught a small rainbow trout.

He was absolutely beautiful. Nate taught me how to gently catch him, and we took a quick picture. I set him back down in the water, but he immediately flipped over on his back and seemed paralyzed. In an instant, Nate flipped him back over and held him for a second, until the fish regained his breath and swam off. He explained to me that fish will do that if not placed back properly in the water.

I realized I had a lot in common with that rainbow trout. The shock of cancer had pulled me out of my comfort zone, and after all the surgeries and the struggles, I had finally been returned to the stream of my life. So many loved ones, so many God appointments, so many experiences had surrounded me, held me, gave me a chance to catch my breath, and propelled me back into life.

Time has a healing quality. Life may not look like it once did, but honestly, I wouldn't have wanted it to. It now had much deeper meaning. I valued it more. I valued myself more. I didn't tolerate the things I once did.

I was learning I could go it alone. I didn't have to have a partner or husband to be valuable. I didn't have to live someone else's dreams or sacrifice my desires. I didn't have to sleep next to someone to feel love. I didn't have to go out of my way to fulfill what others expected of me. Even though there were still moments when I really wanted to be a wife, I knew now I couldn't make that happen. I couldn't control the outcome.

Time has a healing quality.
I valued my life more. I valued
myself more. I didn't tolerate
the things I once did. I was
learning I could go it alone.

One thing I could do, however, was love myself. Rather than expect someone to do it for me, I could buy myself flowers, go to a movie, or take a trip to the beach.

I could believe I was enough just as I am. My value was not determined by my social status, my car, my resume, my weight, what I did for others, how much money I have in the bank, or the size of my house. I AM enough. Just me.

I was learning to trust that life wants us to succeed—that we are all on the path to be what we are meant to be, and that nothing can get in the way of that.

Part of loving myself was ultimately deciding to move closer to my daughters in Los Angeles. That move took a lot of courage. I got my California real estate license and moved to the Hollywood Hills. I've been here a year, and it has been a wonderful year of more growth for me. I found an awesome brokerage and made new friends. I've even taken some acting classes, and classes on public speaking. I've learned how to be independent and to do loving things for myself. I love hiking and riding my bike along the ocean. I love hearing music at the Hollywood Bowl. It's pretty exciting to run into Jack Black or Christopher Nolan in my neighborhood.

I received so many gifts on that trip to Colorado. But the biggest gift of all was realizing my life was a gift. And it was already mine to enjoy.

To love yourself, you must first believe you are worthy of love. You are worthy of doing the kind of work that feeds your soul. You are worthy of being in a healthy relationship filled with love. You are worthy to travel and see the things you've always wanted to see. You are worthy of walking along the beach and just being. You are worthy of rest. You are worthy of being healed. By nurturing self-love, you build resilience and confidence. You've got this!

What makes you feel truly loved? How can you love and appreciate yourself more today?

_____

_____

_____

_____

CONCLUSION

THE MIRACLE

Miracles rest not so much upon healing power,
coming suddenly near us from afar, but upon
our perceptions being made finer, so that for
the moment our eyes can see and our ears can
hear what has been there around us, always.

WILLA CATHER

In all, my cancer journey took me through six surgeries. It took me two years to really feel like my brain was firing on all cylinders again. But eventually, it did. If you're still in surgery fog and it seems like it's been a long time since you've been firing

The miracle is life itself.

The miracle is me—and you.

on all cylinders, have patience with yourself. You'll get your spark back.

I got my spark back by realizing that the miracle isn't perfect health, or a loving relationship, or the meaningful career.

The miracle is life itself. The miracle is me—and you.

Now, I work on being thankful for the life I currently have, and for the opportunity to keep living. I write goals on a whiteboard in my office, and I look at them every day, sometimes more than once a day. Those goals help me appreciate my opportunities to live and dream. I write goals that will challenge me and push me—travel goals, health goals, writing goals, and real estate goals.

Discovering what makes you happy, what you can do to love yourself, and continuing to dream all will help you get your spark back. That may be a car metaphor, but I believe that whenever we think of something bigger than ourselves, it sparks us to do more and to dream bigger. That's the sweet spot in life.

It doesn't matter what you do for a living, how much money you make, whether you're in a committed

Discovering what makes you happy, what you can do to love yourself, and continuing to dream all will help you get your spark back.

relationship, or what kind of cancer treatment you choose—it just matters whether you're living fully as your authentic self.

If we fight for who we are and the purpose we are here to fulfill, one day we will realize we are not broken beyond repair. We are enough just the way we are. Not because of something we have or do. We are enough in our humanity. When we honor our story and the stories of others, that's the gold—the depth of what we've gone through and the depth of what others have gone through, too. Hopefully our journeys can comingle harmoniously and we can help one another grow.

I hope my story will help you honor your own story. I hope it inspires you to continue fighting for your purpose.

Remember who you were as you were growing up. You were brave and full of hope. You probably loved to create art and dance and laugh. You dreamed big. You were courageous.

Things are just things, and getting more of them will not make you happy. Feeding your soul is the way to be happy, along with listening to a Higher Power (God). Stay out of your ego as much as possible. Work

Even in the turmoil of cancer, there are pools of joy and hope and peace. Even in the uncertainty, there is love.

on "being" instead of doing. (That's a tough one for me.) Work on creating and appreciating beauty. Turn on your favorite music and just dance. Sing loudly in your car; you may inspire someone.

Realize you have a purpose for being here. You are special and important, and no one can replace you. You were meant to be. Learn to be good to yourself. Love yourself. If you don't love yourself first, you won't have anything to give others.

Be there for yourself and others as we all do our best to navigate the waters of a life well lived. It's a journey worth taking. Even in the turmoil of cancer, there are pools of joy and hope and peace. Even in the uncertainty, there is love.

I wrote this poem later in my healing journey:

I see the sun, the sky, the clouds, and I welcome you in.

LIFE! I welcome you.

I hold you with a warm hug, and I kiss your cheek sweetly.

Thank you for coming.

We sit and sip our tea and laugh.

Oh, it's so nice to be together.

I'm looking forward to many more of these . . .

All you need to do to receive your miracle is realize it's already here. The miracle is you. Show up in your life, whatever it looks like, and live fully now.

ACKNOWLEDGMENTS

I am grateful to God for nudging me to write this book and for healing my body and soul.

Thank you to my sweet daughters, Liz and Sarah, who have stood beside me. They are the light of my life, and they are always my "why." I love you. I am so grateful for you.

Thank you to Lexie and Roxie for your encouragement; you have brought so much joy to my life, and I am grateful for you.

Thank you to my wonderful editor, Amanda Rooker, who helped me along this journey. I'm very thankful that you "see" me and have helped me get this book completed.

I am very appreciative of the doctors and nurses at Vanderbilt and their care. Thank you especially to Dr. Higdon.

Thank you to Gilda's Club and all the various breast cancer support groups that played a part in my healing.

I would like to acknowledge Dr. Bongani Msungane Kaimila from Lilongwe, Malawi, for his wisdom and encouraging words. He has passed away, but his influence lives on.

Thank you to my mother for her enduring support and love. I miss you.

Thank you to my dear friends Cindy and Heather for their love and encouragement.

Thank you to the Franklin High School girls lacrosse team for all the nurturing, healthy meals.

Thank you to my counselors Jennifer and Zahra for being so loving.

Thank you to Ashley Peed from The Daily Pursuit for being such a great health coach.

Thank you to all the people who prayed for me and with me.

Thank you to Sissy, Teena, Carla, Tina, Margaret, Mary, Zenya, Kelly, and Stella, my friends new and old who are so encouraging.

Thank you, Brenda and Suzanne, for being there early on in the journey.

Thank you, Hoda Kotb, for giving me your pink hope ring when we met. You are an inspiration.

Thank you to Al Roker and the whole *Today* family—you made me feel less alone, and I am thankful for you guys.

Thank you to Tracie and all the survivors who walked alongside me.

Thank you to Grace Center, Christ Community Church, and Church of the City for being my places of worship.

Thank you to the sweet city of Franklin, Tennessee, which I called home for twenty-five years.

Thank you to David Bilger and Griefshare who helped so much after Mom's passing.

Thank you to my sweet fur babies: Miles, Oliver, and Rudy.

Thank you to the Nashville Philharmonic Orchestra for letting me sit in on that one series. Playing the viola gives me great joy.

Thank you to the Nashville Symphony Chorus soprano section for ten years of joy.

Thank you to the people in my life who taught me great lessons—you know who you are.

Thank you to my new friends Dr. Maria Nemeth of Academy for Coaching Excellence and Brandon Gaydorus of Warm Heart Life. You both have made a huge difference in my life.

Thank you to Nourmand and Associates for welcoming me with open arms to Los Angeles.

ABOUT THE AUTHOR

Heather Thurman is a two-time cancer survivor, single mom, and licensed Realtor. Her purpose is to inspire others to live their best lives, overcome obstacles, and be a positive force in their communities. Heather loves to sing in her community choir, hike, travel, volunteer, listen to live music, write, and spend time with her daughters, friends and sweet dog Oliver. She is also passionate about real estate in Los Angeles and enjoying the beauty of the area. Contact her at thelittlebookofhealing@gmail.com.

Milton Keynes UK
Ingram Content Group UK Ltd.
UKHW020730010424
440421UK00014B/730